D1111638

Travel Junkie

The History of Me

MY TRAVEL LOG

ADVENTURE AWAITS IF YOU DARE

COLLECT YOUR MEMORIES.
YOUR WORDS. YOUR PAGES.
BOOKS WITH SOUL.COM
COPYRIGHT 2019

978-1-949325-54-6

"" ONCE A YEAR, GO SOMEPLACE YOU'VE NEVER BEEN BEFORE." DALAI LAMA

FOR

FROM

IF YOU WANT
TO PRESERVE
YOUR
MEMORIES
YOU CAN

THE HISTORY OF ME

Go. See. Do. Remember. Let's do it.
We spend our time and money preparing for fantasy trips, weekend getaways, and family vacations we think we will never forget. But unfortunately with time, you forget that adorable man who carried your luggage on his donkey, and the name of that cute little mom and pop hotel with the softest sheets. If you had one book to record the important facts about each and every trip, well…can you say priceless?
Take the time to record your vacations, voyages, road-trips and adventures. Collect and preserve your memories.
In this Travel Log, you can organize and log 50 trips, weekend getaways, and wild adventures:

Section 1:
A section to write down a master list of every adventure you take. If you don't take the time to complete the rest of the book, at least record the date and place of your next 50 trips and adventures.

Section 2:
For each trip, there are two pages with prompts and questions that will help you record important facts and memories. Complete the two pages on the way home from the trip or before you unpack.
Make it a habit, and soon you will fill the pages of this book with treasured memories. Memories you will remember and pass on to friends, family and even children.

Section 3:
Pages to create a travel wish list, a great reference page, to use when you are planning your next 50 trips.
Here We Go!

50 TRIPS & ADVENTURES

DATE	PLACE

50 TRIPS & ADVENTURES

DATE	PLACE

DATE- MODE OF TRANSPORTATION

THIS IS WHERE I WENT!

WHERE I SLEPT

WHO I MET

DETAILS WORTH REMEMBERING

EXPERIENCES I CAN'T FORGET- A FIRST FOR ME

WHAT I ATE

FAVORITE MOMENT OF THE TRIP--I LOVED THIS

DATE- MODE OF TRANSPORTATION

THIS IS WHERE I WENT!

WHERE I SLEPT

WHO I MET

DETAILS WORTH REMEMBERING

EXPERIENCES I CAN'T FORGET- A FIRST FOR ME

WHAT I ATE

FAVORITE MOMENT OF THE TRIP--I LOVED THIS

DATE- MODE OF TRANSPORTATION ------- - - -- --- --- --- --

THIS IS WHERE I WENT!

WHERE I SLEPT

WHO I MET

DETAILS WORTH REMEMBERING

EXPERIENCES I CAN'T FORGET- A FIRST FOR ME

WHAT I ATE

FAVORITE MOMENT OF THE TRIP--I LOVED THIS

DATE- MODE OF TRANSPORTATION

THIS IS WHERE I WENT!

WHERE I SLEPT

WHO I MET

DETAILS WORTH REMEMBERING

EXPERIENCES I CAN'T FORGET- A FIRST FOR ME

WHAT I ATE

FAVORITE MOMENT OF THE TRIP--I LOVED THIS

DATE- MODE OF TRANSPORTATION

THIS IS WHERE I WENT!

WHERE I SLEPT

WHO I MET

DETAILS WORTH REMEMBERING

EXPERIENCES I CAN'T FORGET- A FIRST FOR ME

WHAT I ATE

FAVORITE MOMENT OF THE TRIP--I LOVED THIS

"THE FIRST CONDITION
OF UNDERSTANDING A
FOREIGN COUNTRY IS
TO SMELL IT."
RUDYARD KIPLING

DATE- MODE OF TRANSPORTATION

THIS IS WHERE I WENT!

WHERE I SLEPT

WHO I MET

DETAILS WORTH REMEMBERING

EXPERIENCES I CAN'T FORGET- A FIRST FOR ME

WHAT I ATE

FAVORITE MOMENT OF THE TRIP--I LOVED THIS

DATE- MODE OF TRANSPORTATION

THIS IS WHERE I WENT!

WHERE I SLEPT

WHO I MET

DETAILS WORTH REMEMBERING

EXPERIENCES I CAN'T FORGET- A FIRST FOR ME

WHAT I ATE

FAVORITE MOMENT OF THE TRIP--I LOVED THIS

DATE- MODE OF TRANSPORTATION

THIS IS WHERE I WENT!

WHERE I SLEPT

WHO I MET

DETAILS WORTH REMEMBERING

EXPERIENCES I CAN'T FORGET- A FIRST FOR ME

WHAT I ATE

FAVORITE MOMENT OF THE TRIP--I LOVED THIS

DATE- MODE OF TRANSPORTATION ....

THIS IS WHERE I WENT!

WHERE I SLEPT

WHO I MET

DETAILS WORTH REMEMBERING

EXPERIENCES I CAN'T FORGET- A FIRST FOR ME

WHAT I ATE

FAVORITE MOMENT OF THE TRIP--I LOVED THIS

DATE- MODE OF TRANSPORTATION

THIS IS WHERE I WENT!

WHERE I SLEPT

WHO I MET

DETAILS WORTH REMEMBERING

EXPERIENCES I CAN'T FORGET- A FIRST FOR ME

WHAT I ATE

FAVORITE MOMENT OF THE TRIP--I LOVED THIS

"TWO ROADS DIVERGED
IN A WOOD, AND I
I TOOK THE ONE LESS
TRAVELED BY, AND
THAT HAS MADE ALL
THE DIFFERENCE."
ROBERT FROST

DATE- MODE OF TRANSPORTATION

THIS IS WHERE I WENT!

WHERE I SLEPT

WHO I MET

DETAILS WORTH REMEMBERING

EXPERIENCES I CAN'T FORGET- A FIRST FOR ME

WHAT I ATE

FAVORITE MOMENT OF THE TRIP--I LOVED THIS

DATE- MODE OF TRANSPORTATION

THIS IS WHERE I WENT!

WHERE I SLEPT

WHO I MET

DETAILS WORTH REMEMBERING

EXPERIENCES I CAN'T FORGET- A FIRST FOR ME

WHAT I ATE

FAVORITE MOMENT OF THE TRIP--I LOVED THIS

DATE- MODE OF TRANSPORTATION

THIS IS WHERE I WENT!

WHERE I SLEPT

WHO I MET

DETAILS WORTH REMEMBERING

EXPERIENCES I CAN'T FORGET- A FIRST FOR ME

WHAT I ATE

FAVORITE MOMENT OF THE TRIP--I LOVED THIS

DATE- MODE OF TRANSPORTATION

THIS IS WHERE I WENT!

WHERE I SLEPT

WHO I MET

DETAILS WORTH REMEMBERING

EXPERIENCES I CAN'T FORGET- A FIRST FOR ME

WHAT I ATE

FAVORITE MOMENT OF THE TRIP--I LOVED THIS

DATE- MODE OF TRANSPORTATION

THIS IS WHERE I WENT!

WHERE I SLEPT

WHO I MET

DETAILS WORTH REMEMBERING

EXPERIENCES I CAN'T FORGET– A FIRST FOR ME

WHAT I ATE

FAVORITE MOMENT OF THE TRIP--I LOVED THIS

"FOR MY PART, I TRAVEL
NOT TO GO ANYWHERE,
BUT TO GO. I TRAVEL
FOR TRAVEL'S SAKE.
THE GREAT AFFAIR IS
TO MOVE."
ROBERT LOUIS
STEVENSON

DATE- MODE OF TRANSPORTATION

THIS IS WHERE I WENT!

WHERE I SLEPT

WHO I MET

DETAILS WORTH REMEMBERING

EXPERIENCES I CAN'T FORGET- A FIRST FOR ME

WHAT I ATE

FAVORITE MOMENT OF THE TRIP--I LOVED THIS

DATE- MODE OF TRANSPORTATION

THIS IS WHERE I WENT!

WHERE I SLEPT

WHO I MET

DETAILS WORTH REMEMBERING

EXPERIENCES I CAN'T FORGET- A FIRST FOR ME

WHAT I ATE

FAVORITE MOMENT OF THE TRIP--I LOVED THIS

DATE- MODE OF TRANSPORTATION

THIS IS WHERE I WENT!

WHERE I SLEPT

WHO I MET

DETAILS WORTH REMEMBERING

EXPERIENCES I CAN'T FORGET- A FIRST FOR ME

WHAT I ATE

FAVORITE MOMENT OF THE TRIP--I LOVED THIS

DATE- MODE OF TRANSPORTATION

THIS IS WHERE I WENT!

WHERE I SLEPT

WHO I MET

DETAILS WORTH REMEMBERING

EXPERIENCES I CAN'T FORGET- A FIRST FOR ME

WHAT I ATE

FAVORITE MOMENT OF THE TRIP--I LOVED THIS

DATE- MODE OF TRANSPORTATION

THIS IS WHERE I WENT!

WHERE I SLEPT

WHO I MET

DETAILS WORTH REMEMBERING

EXPERIENCES I CAN'T FORGET- A FIRST FOR ME

WHAT I ATE

FAVORITE MOMENT OF THE TRIP--I LOVED THIS

"TRAVEL, IN THE
YOUNGER SORT, IS A
PART OF EDUCATION IN
THE ELDER, A PART OF
THE EXPERIENCE."
FRANCIS BACON

DATE- MODE OF TRANSPORTATION

THIS IS WHERE I WENT!

WHERE I SLEPT

WHO I MET

DETAILS WORTH REMEMBERING

EXPERIENCES I CAN'T FORGET- A FIRST FOR ME

WHAT I ATE

FAVORITE MOMENT OF THE TRIP--I LOVED THIS

DATE- MODE OF TRANSPORTATION

THIS IS WHERE I WENT!

WHERE I SLEPT

WHO I MET

DETAILS WORTH REMEMBERING

EXPERIENCES I CAN'T FORGET- A FIRST FOR ME

WHAT I ATE

FAVORITE MOMENT OF THE TRIP--I LOVED THIS

DATE- MODE OF TRANSPORTATION

THIS IS WHERE I WENT!

WHERE I SLEPT

WHO I MET

DETAILS WORTH REMEMBERING

EXPERIENCES I CAN'T FORGET- A FIRST FOR ME

WHAT I ATE

FAVORITE MOMENT OF THE TRIP--I LOVED THIS

DATE- MODE OF TRANSPORTATION - - - - - - - - - - - - - - - - - -

THIS IS WHERE I WENT!

WHERE I SLEPT

WHO I MET

DETAILS WORTH REMEMBERING

EXPERIENCES I CAN'T FORGET- A FIRST FOR ME

WHAT I ATE

FAVORITE MOMENT OF THE TRIP--I LOVED THIS

DATE- MODE OF TRANSPORTATION

THIS IS WHERE I WENT!

WHERE I SLEPT

WHO I MET

DETAILS WORTH REMEMBERING

EXPERIENCES I CAN'T FORGET- A FIRST FOR ME

WHAT I ATE

FAVORITE MOMENT OF THE TRIP--I LOVED THIS

"TO TRAVEL IS TO LOVE,
LEARN, AND LIVE
OUTSIDE YOUR SELF."
A.K. SMITH

DATE- MODE OF TRANSPORTATION

THIS IS WHERE I WENT!

WHERE I SLEPT

WHO I MET

DETAILS WORTH REMEMBERING

EXPERIENCES I CAN'T FORGET- A FIRST FOR ME

WHAT I ATE

FAVORITE MOMENT OF THE TRIP--I LOVED THIS

DATE- MODE OF TRANSPORTATION

THIS IS WHERE I WENT!

WHERE I SLEPT

WHO I MET

DETAILS WORTH REMEMBERING

EXPERIENCES I CAN'T FORGET- A FIRST FOR ME

WHAT I ATE

FAVORITE MOMENT OF THE TRIP--I LOVED THIS

DATE- MODE OF TRANSPORTATION

THIS IS WHERE I WENT!

WHERE I SLEPT

WHO I MET

DETAILS WORTH REMEMBERING

EXPERIENCES I CAN'T FORGET- A FIRST FOR ME

WHAT I ATE

FAVORITE MOMENT OF THE TRIP--I LOVED THIS

DATE- MODE OF TRANSPORTATION

THIS IS WHERE I WENT!

WHERE I SLEPT

WHO I MET

DETAILS WORTH REMEMBERING

EXPERIENCES I CAN'T FORGET- A FIRST FOR ME

WHAT I ATE

FAVORITE MOMENT OF THE TRIP--I LOVED THIS

DATE- MODE OF TRANSPORTATION

THIS IS WHERE I WENT!

WHERE I SLEPT

WHO I MET

DETAILS WORTH REMEMBERING

EXPERIENCES I CAN'T FORGET- A FIRST FOR ME

WHAT I ATE

FAVORITE MOMENT OF THE TRIP--I LOVED THIS

"THE WORLD IS A BOOK
AND THOSE WHO DO
NOT TRAVEL READ
ONLY A PAGE."
SAINT AUGUSTINE

DATE- MODE OF TRANSPORTATION

THIS IS WHERE I WENT!

WHERE I SLEPT

WHO I MET

DETAILS WORTH REMEMBERING

EXPERIENCES I CAN'T FORGET- A FIRST FOR ME

WHAT I ATE

FAVORITE MOMENT OF THE TRIP--I LOVED THIS

DATE- MODE OF TRANSPORTATION

THIS IS WHERE I WENT!

WHERE I SLEPT

WHO I MET

DETAILS WORTH REMEMBERING

EXPERIENCES I CAN'T FORGET- A FIRST FOR ME

WHAT I ATE

FAVORITE MOMENT OF THE TRIP--I LOVED THIS

DATE- MODE OF TRANSPORTATION

THIS IS WHERE I WENT!

WHERE I SLEPT

WHO I MET

DETAILS WORTH REMEMBERING

EXPERIENCES I CAN'T FORGET- A FIRST FOR ME

WHAT I ATE

FAVORITE MOMENT OF THE TRIP--I LOVED THIS

DATE- MODE OF TRANSPORTATION

THIS IS WHERE I WENT!

WHERE I SLEPT

WHO I MET

DETAILS WORTH REMEMBERING

EXPERIENCES I CAN'T FORGET- A FIRST FOR ME

WHAT I ATE

FAVORITE MOMENT OF THE TRIP--I LOVED THIS

DATE- MODE OF TRANSPORTATION ....

THIS IS WHERE I WENT!

WHERE I SLEPT

WHO I MET

DETAILS WORTH REMEMBERING

EXPERIENCES I CAN'T FORGET- A FIRST FOR ME

WHAT I ATE

FAVORITE MOMENT OF THE TRIP--I LOVED THIS

"THE JOURNEY NOT THE
ARRIVAL MATTERS."
T.S. ELIOT

DATE- MODE OF TRANSPORTATION

THIS IS WHERE I WENT!

WHERE I SLEPT

WHO I MET

DETAILS WORTH REMEMBERING

EXPERIENCES I CAN'T FORGET- A FIRST FOR ME

WHAT I ATE

FAVORITE MOMENT OF THE TRIP--I LOVED THIS

DATE- MODE OF TRANSPORTATION

THIS IS WHERE I WENT!

WHERE I SLEPT

WHO I MET

DETAILS WORTH REMEMBERING

EXPERIENCES I CAN'T FORGET- A FIRST FOR ME

WHAT I ATE

FAVORITE MOMENT OF THE TRIP--I LOVED THIS

DATE- MODE OF TRANSPORTATION

THIS IS WHERE I WENT!

WHERE I SLEPT

WHO I MET

DETAILS WORTH REMEMBERING

EXPERIENCES I CAN'T FORGET- A FIRST FOR ME

WHAT I ATE

FAVORITE MOMENT OF THE TRIP--I LOVED THIS

DATE- MODE OF TRANSPORTATION

THIS IS WHERE I WENT!

WHERE I SLEPT

WHO I MET

DETAILS WORTH REMEMBERING

EXPERIENCES I CAN'T FORGET- A FIRST FOR ME

WHAT I ATE

FAVORITE MOMENT OF THE TRIP--I LOVED THIS

DATE- MODE OF TRANSPORTATION

THIS IS WHERE I WENT!

WHERE I SLEPT

WHO I MET

DETAILS WORTH REMEMBERING

EXPERIENCES I CAN'T FORGET- A FIRST FOR ME

WHAT I ATE

FAVORITE MOMENT OF THE TRIP--I LOVED THIS

DATE- MODE OF TRANSPORTATION

THIS IS WHERE I WENT!

WHERE I SLEPT

WHO I MET

DETAILS WORTH REMEMBERING

EXPERIENCES I CAN'T FORGET- A FIRST FOR ME

WHAT I ATE

FAVORITE MOMENT OF THE TRIP--I LOVED THIS

"A GOOD TRAVELER HAS
NO FIXED PLANS, AND
IS NOT INTENT ON
ARRIVING."
LAO TZU

DATE- MODE OF TRANSPORTATION

THIS IS WHERE I WENT!

WHERE I SLEPT

WHO I MET

DETAILS WORTH REMEMBERING

EXPERIENCES I CAN'T FORGET- A FIRST FOR ME

WHAT I ATE

FAVORITE MOMENT OF THE TRIP--I LOVED THIS

DATE- MODE OF TRANSPORTATION ....

THIS IS WHERE I WENT!

WHERE I SLEPT

WHO I MET

DETAILS WORTH REMEMBERING

EXPERIENCES I CAN'T FORGET- A FIRST FOR ME

WHAT I ATE

FAVORITE MOMENT OF THE TRIP--I LOVED THIS

DATE- MODE OF TRANSPORTATION

THIS IS WHERE I WENT!

WHERE I SLEPT

WHO I MET

DETAILS WORTH REMEMBERING

EXPERIENCES I CAN'T FORGET- A FIRST FOR ME

WHAT I ATE

FAVORITE MOMENT OF THE TRIP--I LOVED THIS

DATE- MODE OF TRANSPORTATION

THIS IS WHERE I WENT!

WHERE I SLEPT

WHO I MET

DETAILS WORTH REMEMBERING

EXPERIENCES I CAN'T FORGET- A FIRST FOR ME

WHAT I ATE

FAVORITE MOMENT OF THE TRIP--I LOVED THIS

DATE- MODE OF TRANSPORTATION

THIS IS WHERE I WENT!

WHERE I SLEPT

WHO I MET

DETAILS WORTH REMEMBERING

EXPERIENCES I CAN'T FORGET- A FIRST FOR ME

WHAT I ATE

FAVORITE MOMENT OF THE TRIP--I LOVED THIS

"THE TRAVELER SEES
WHAT HE SEES, THE
TOURIST SEES WHAT HE
HAS COME TO SEE."
G.K. CHESTERTON

DATE- MODE OF TRANSPORTATION

THIS IS WHERE I WENT!

WHERE I SLEPT

WHO I MET

DETAILS WORTH REMEMBERING

EXPERIENCES I CAN'T FORGET- A FIRST FOR ME

WHAT I ATE

FAVORITE MOMENT OF THE TRIP--I LOVED THIS

DATE- MODE OF TRANSPORTATION -

THIS IS WHERE I WENT!

WHERE I SLEPT

WHO I MET

DETAILS WORTH REMEMBERING

EXPERIENCES I CAN'T FORGET- A FIRST FOR ME

WHAT I ATE

FAVORITE MOMENT OF THE TRIP--I LOVED THIS

DATE- MODE OF TRANSPORTATION

THIS IS WHERE I WENT!

WHERE I SLEPT

WHO I MET

DETAILS WORTH REMEMBERING

EXPERIENCES I CAN'T FORGET- A FIRST FOR ME

WHAT I ATE

FAVORITE MOMENT OF THE TRIP--I LOVED THIS

DATE- MODE OF TRANSPORTATION

THIS IS WHERE I WENT!

WHERE I SLEPT

WHO I MET

DETAILS WORTH REMEMBERING

EXPERIENCES I CAN'T FORGET- A FIRST FOR ME

WHAT I ATE

FAVORITE MOMENT OF THE TRIP--I LOVED THIS

DATE- MODE OF TRANSPORTATION

THIS IS WHERE I WENT!

WHERE I SLEPT

WHO I MET

DETAILS WORTH REMEMBERING

EXPERIENCES I CAN'T FORGET- A FIRST FOR ME

WHAT I ATE

FAVORITE MOMENT OF THE TRIP--I LOVED THIS

DATE- MODE OF TRANSPORTATION

THIS IS WHERE I WENT!

WHERE I SLEPT

WHO I MET

DETAILS WORTH REMEMBERING

EXPERIENCES I CAN'T FORGET- A FIRST FOR ME

WHAT I ATE

FAVORITE MOMENT OF THE TRIP--I LOVED THIS

LIST OF ALL THE COUNTRIES
IN THE WORLD

A
AFGHANISTAN
ALBANIA
ALGERIA
ANDORRA
ANGOLA
ANTIGUA AND BARBUDA
ARGENTINA
ARMENIA
ARUBA
AUSTRALIA
AUSTRIA
AZERBAIJAN
B
BAHAMAS, THE
BAHRAIN
BANGLADESH
BARBADOS
BELARUS
BELGIUM
BELIZE
BENIN
BHUTAN
BOLIVIA
BOSNIA AND HERZEGOVINA
BOTSWANA
BRAZIL
BRUNEI
BULGARIA
BURKINA FASO
BURMA
BURUNDI

C

CAMBODIA

CAMEROON

CANADA

CABO VERDE

CENTRAL AFRICAN
REPUBLIC

CHAD

CHILE

CHINA

COLOMBIA

COMOROS

CONGO, DEMOCRATIC
REPUBLIC OF THE

CONGO, REPUBLIC OF THE

COSTA RICA

COTE D'IVOIRE

CROATIA

CUBA

CURACAO

CYPRUS

CZECHIA

D

DENMARK

DJIBOUTI

DOMINICA

DOMINICAN REPUBLIC

E

EAST TIMOR SEE TIMOR-
LESTE

ECUADOR

EGYPT

EL SALVADOR

EQUATORIAL GUINEA

ERITREA

ESTONIA

ETHIOPIA

F

FIJI

FINLAND

FRANCE

G

GABON

GAMBIA THE

GEORGIA

GERMANY

GHANA

GREECE

GRENADA

GUATEMALA

GUINEA

GUINEA-BISSAU

GUYANA

H

HAITI

HOLY SEE

HONDURAS

HONG KONG

HUNGARY

I

ICELAND

INDIA

INDONESIA

IRAN

IRAQ

IRELAND

ISRAEL

ITALY

J

JAMAICA

JAPAN

JORDAN

K

KAZAKHTAN

KENYA

K

KIRIBATI

KOREA, NORTH

KOREA, SOUTH

KOSOVO

KUWAIT

KYRGYZSTAN

L

LAOS

LATVIA

LEBANON

LESOTHO

LIBERIA

LIBYA

LIECHTENSTEIN

LITHUANIA

LUXEMBOURG

M

MACAU

MACEDONIA

MADAGASCAR

MALAWI

MALAYSIA

MALDIVES

MALI

MALTA

MARSHALL ISLANDS

MAURITANIA

MAURITIUS

MEXICO

MICRONESIA

MOLDOVA

MONACO

MONGOLIA

MONTENEGRO

MOROCCO

MOZAMBIQUE

N
NAMIBIA
NAURU
NEPAL
NETHERLANDS
NEW ZEALAND
NICARAGUA
NIGER
NIGERIA
NORTH KOREA
NORWAY
O
OMAN
P
PAKISTAN
PALAU
PALESTINIAN TERRITORIES
PANAMA
PAPUA NEW GUINEA
PARAGUAY
PERU
PHILIPPINES
POLAND
PORTUGAL
Q
QATAR
R
ROMANIA
RUSSIA
RWANDA
S
SAINT KITTS AND NEVIS
SAINT LUCIA
SAINT VINCENT AND THE
GRENADINES
SAMOA

S

SAO TOME AND PRINCIPE

SAUDI ARABIA

SENEGAL

SERBIA

SEYCHELLES

SIERRA LEONE

SINGAPORE

SINT MAARTEN

SLOVAKIA

SLOVENIA

SOLOMON ISLANDS

SOMALIA

SOUTH AFRICA

SOUTH KOREA

SOUTH SUDAN

SPAIN

SRI LANKA

SUDAN

SURINAME

SWAZILAND

SWEDEN

SWITZERLAND

SYRIA

T

TAIWAN

TAJIKISTAN

TANZANIA

THAILAND

TIMOR-LESTE

TOGO

TONGA

TRINIDAD AND TOBAGO

TUNISIA

TURKEY

TURKMENISTAN

TUVALU

U
UGANDA
UKRAINE
UNITED ARAB EMIRATES
UNITED KINGDOM
URUGUAY
UZBEKISTAN
V
VANUATU
VENEZUELA
VIETNAM

Y
YEMEN
Z
ZAMBIA
ZIMBABWE

CIRCLE THE COUNTRIES YOU WANT TO VISIT.
LOOK UP THE ONES YOU NEVER HEARD OF.
PICK ONE COUNTRY THAT IS THE
ROAD LESS TRAVELED AND HAVE AN ADVENTURE OF A
LIFETIME.

THE LIST OF COUNTRIES CAN DIFFER FROM DIFFERENT
SOURCES. THIS LIST IS FROM

THE U.S. DEPARTMENT OF STATE.
HTTPS WWW.STATE.GOV MISC LIST INDEX.HTM

TRAVEL WISH LIST

TRAVEL WISH LIST

TRAVEL WISH LIST

TRAVEL WISH LIST

CHECK OUT OTHER GIFT BOOKS AND JOURNALS
AMAZON.COM AUTHOR BOOKSWITHSOUL
OR GO TO BOOKSWITHSOUL.COM

WHEN WE WERE ONE..PREGNANCY JOURNAL
OLD SOUL NOTEBOOK OF IDEAS FROM AN OLD SOUL
SERIOUSLY YOUR 50?
GRATITUDE JOURNAL I CAN ONLY IMAGINE
MY FUTURE JOURNAL POSSIBILITIES
POSITIVITY JOURNAL JUST BREATH
BOOKS WITH SOUL ANNIVERSARY SERIES
EVERY BREATH A JOURNAL OF GRATITUDE & POSSIBILITIES
MUSIC JOURNAL MY MUSIC JOURNEY
HUNTING SEASON LOG BOOK FACT OR FICTION
UNICORNS ARE REAL STORY NOTEBOOK SERIES
BABY SHARKS ARE REAL STORY NOTEBOOK SERIES
REFLECTIONS FROM THE BEACH

Made in the USA
Coppell, TX
06 May 2020